He was sent away.

Four little angels
in the Christmas play.
One had a runny nose.

She was sent away.

Three little angels
in the Christmas play.
One pulled a wing off.

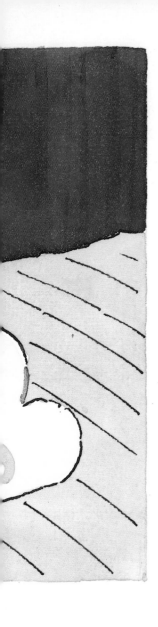

She was sent away.

Two little angels
in the Christmas play.
One pushed the cloud down.

He was sent away.

One little angel
in the Christmas play.
She was sad and lonely.

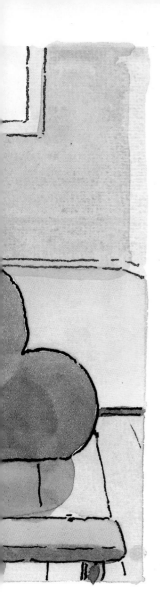

She cried and ran
away.

No little angels
in the Christmas play.
Mrs Best was very sad.

13

Five little angels
back in the Christmas play.

15

The mums and dads
all came to watch.